Worms Can't Fly

Teenage author Aislinn O'Loughlin is well-known for her hilariously quirky and fast-paced reworkings of famous fairy tales. Her first book, *Cinderella's Fella*, was written when she was only fourteen; her second, *A Right Royal Pain: The True Story of Rumpelstiltskin* (selected as a White Raven book by international librarians), followed only a few months later. *The Emperor's Birthday Suit* and *Shak & the Beanstalk* were published in 1997, and *Fionn the Cool* in 1998 (all available from Wolfhound Press). Aislinn lives in Templeogue and is studying at University College Dublin.

Larry O'Loughlin is a storyteller and author of five books for younger children; he is also co-author of *Our House*, a non-fiction book for adults. One of his titles for younger children, *The Gobán Saor*, illustrated by John Leonard, was short-listed for the 1997 Bisto Book of the Year Award. His first book for teenagers, *Is Anybody Listening?* was published by Wolfhound Press in 1999. Larry lives in Dublin with his wife and family, one of whom is Aislinn.

Worms Can't Fly

Aislinn & Larry O'Loughlin

WOLFHOUND PRESS
Celebrating 25 *Years*

First published in 2000 by
Wolfhound Press Ltd
68 Mountjoy Square
Dublin 1, Ireland
Tel: (353-1) 874 0354
Fax: (353-1) 872 0207

The Arts Council
An Chomhairle Ealaíon

Wolfhound Press receives financial assistance from
The Arts Council/An Chomhairle Ealaíon, Dublin, Ireland.

British Library Cataloguing in Publication Data
A catalogue record for this book is available from the British Library.

ISBN 0-86327-786-1

10 9 8 7 6 5 4 3 2 1

Cover Illustration & Design: Aileen Caffrey
Typesetting: Wolfhound Press
Printed in the UK by Cox & Wyman Ltd, Reading, Berks.

Contents

To Pat Kenny,
for giving us the first push forward
in our poetic career.

Also, to Sarah Webb, Deirdre Whelan, Eilís French, Nuala Lyons, Ger Whelan, Jerry Naughton, Monica O'Loughlin, Róisín O'Loughlin, Sinéad O'Loughlin, Seán O'Loughlin, Jenni O'Loughlin, everyone of O'Loughlin and Naughton descent/name, John Molloy, Kim and Sheba, Dreyfus the Goldfish (R.I.P.), MacDara MacUibhAille (no, we can't pronounce it either!), Marie-Louise Fitzpatrick, John Leonard, Pierce and Gail, Gail and Marcos (different Gail), Ash (from Larry), Dad (from Aislinn), Hugh Scott, all of Wolfhound Press, Orwell Writers Group (R.I.P.), CBI, everyone who ever had anything to do with us in school, everyone from every school we've ever visited, UCD Dramsoc, God, Britney Spears, Virgil, Homer, Thucydides, Santa Claus, the Easter Bunny, the Tooth Fairy, Father Time, the Ghosts of Christmas Past, Present and Yet-to-Come, you, the guy from the Diet Coke ads, Darth Vader, Peter Pan, Babe the Talking Pig, the genius who invented chocolate milkshakes, the nice man who works in the vegetable shop, the guy who delivers the milk to Number 63, and the beetle I accidentally trod on this morning.

There — now we never have to dedicate a book
to anyone ever again!

Worms Can't Fly

If worms can't fly,
then tell me, please,
why do birds
wait in trees?

9

In My Own Words

Teacher's really angry —
he's making me stay after school
and write a trillion million times,
'I mustn't play the fool.'

But I wasn't being silly,
I wasn't being bold,
I was only trying
to do what I was told.

He read us a poem and said,
'Write that in your own words.'
And now he's angry 'cause I wrote,
'Nixscubble bixsnix scurds.'

Our Dog

Our dog has no nose,
never will, never had.
When I'm asked how he smells,
I say, 'Really bad!'

Take Me to Your ... Never Mind

A two-headed alien called Grot,
who looked like a giant blue snot,
opened all six red eyes
and said with surprise,
'Earthlings are an ugly lot!'

Mum!

Mum, make her give my roller-blades back!
She's had them most of the day,
and she keeps skating up and down the road
in this really show-offy way.

She skates right up to the wall next door,
then jumps up and slides 'cross the top,
or rolls down the hill turning somersaults....
Please, Mum, make her stop!

She's spinning around and around on one leg
like she's some champion ice-skater.
She's such a rotten show-off —
I'm really starting to hate her.

Mum, make her give my roller-blades back
and go inside for tea,
and tell her to grow up and act her age —
after all, Granny *is* eighty-three!

Superman and the Baddy

'Tell me,' said the baddy,
as Superman read him his rights,
'if you're so clever, why are you wearing
your underpants over your tights?'

Dear Teacher

Thank you for bringing all your class
to see our zoo today.
I'm glad you had a lot of fun,
but I'd just like to say,
something has been not quite right
since your class left the zoo;
I don't know how it happened
and so I'm asking you....

Do you know how the eight white mice
got in the elephant pit?
They weren't in there yesterday.
It's quite odd, isn't it?

Can you tell me how the beehive
got in the kangaroo's pouch?
First I knew, she was hopping mad
and shouting, 'Ouch ouch ouch!'

Who taught our parrot those new words?
I just don't have a clue,
But he used to say, 'Pretty Polly!'
and now he says, 'Knickers to you!'

Who put chilli on the penguins' fish?
That's against every rule!
They took one bite, blew smoke from their ears,
and drank down half the pool!

That's all I have to say now —
I really have to go.
I hope that you can help me out.
Signed,

     Zookeeper Joe

P.S. If you find out where our tiger went,
I'd really like to know.

The Cannibal Wedding

At the cannibal wedding
the cry, 'We're all hungry!'
went running around the room.
'Just wait,' said the best man,
'because in a minute
we'll be toasting the bride and the groom.

(And after that we'll stir-fry the bridesmaids.)'

Zebra Crossing

The safest way to cross the road
(I've never seen it fail)
is to find a zebra crossing
and grab onto its tail.

Sing a Song of Sixpence

Sing a song of sixpence,
a pocket full of glee,
the King's cook is in jail
and that's as it should be.

'And let that be a warning,'
said the judge, 'to those who try
to break the law by putting
live blackbirds in a pie.'

21

Aunteater

At Cousin Julie's wedding
I heard somebody scream,
'A great big horrid monster
has just eaten Aunty Jean!'
People rushed in panic,
hiding here and there,
but the monster was too fast for them —
so long, Aunty Clare.
Next it raced past Grandad,
Uncle Mick and Cousin Joe,
and stuck out its big lumpy tongue....
Bye-bye, Aunty Flo.
Then it chewed up Aunties Róisín,
Aislinn and Sinéad —
and then it turned and looked at me.
Gosh, was I afraid!
'Don't worry, it won't hurt us, lad,'
smiled my Uncle Peter.
'I'm an uncle, you're a nephew,
and it's just an aunt-eater.'

Our Dog 2

Our dog chases kids on skates,
he does it every day,
and if he doesn't stop it soon,
I'll take his skates away.

King Kong Konfusion

Henry Herbert Albert White
and Alistair William Wong
both came to my fancy-dress party
dressed up as King Kong.
Their costumes were identical —
same colour, same width, same height —
so no one at the party
could tell Wong from White.

Our Baby

Johnny's baby walks around,
and Aoife's baby speaks,
but Mum should take our baby back,
'cause all it does is leaks.

Mum's a Secret Agent

My mum's a secret agent;
she's got secret-agent things
like recorders in her knickers
and cameras in her rings,
machine-guns in her bracelets,
bazookas in her bra,
and when she takes her necklace off
it turns into a car.
Her fountain-pens fire bullets,
her pencil's a small bomb,
her hearing-aids become hand-grenades
when she turns them on.
Her glasses have got X-ray glass
that sees through walls and stuff;
I tried them on this morning
and saw Grandad in the buff.
Yeah, my mum's a secret agent
and most times that's dead cool,
but I really wish she wasn't
when she writes my notes for school....

ylerecnis sruoY

.nib eht ni ti nworht ev'I won
— yknow lla tnew kcolc mrala ruO
.ni tpels lla ew esuaceb
yadot loohcs rof etal saw yllaS

The Tap-Dancer

Our Rosie was a tap-dancer,
she'd tap the hours away
from sunrise until sunset,
until that fateful day.
Some rotter greased her tap shoes,
and
SPLISH
and
SPLOSH
and
SPLASH —
she slipped and fell right off the taps
and landed in the bath.

A Question of Dogs

If dachshunds dashed
and boxers boxed
and bulldogs all went 'moo'
and wolfhounds howled
and sheepdogs baaed
what would shih-tzus do?

30

Giraffe

'I wonder,' said the field mouse,
looking quite perplexed,
'why it is that all giraffes
have such enormous necks.'

'I know,' said the barn owl.
'At least, I've heard it said,
it's because a giraffe's body
is so far from its head.'

Who Needs Cocoa on the Orinoco?

Down in deepest Venezuela,
A certain Venezuelan sailor
sailed up and down the Orinoco,
eating bread and drinking cocoa,

till a Venezuelan otter
said, 'He is an awful rotter
To tempt us with such rich aromas!'
So he sank his boat and sent him homewards.

Don't Try This at Home

I taught my baby brother to wink —
Mum said I shouldn't try.
But it's not as hard as you would think:
I just poke him in the eye.

The Little Bo Peep Trilogy
(and one more at no extra cost)

Little Bo Peep has lost her sheep,
they're nowhere to be found.
She should ask Jack Horner,
'cause he's on the corner,
selling lamb chops, ten for a pound.

Little Bo Peep has lost her sheep,
and she's feeling quite forlorn,
but she should ask our priest,
'cause he's sick to the teeth
of stray sheep chewing his lawn.

Little Bo Peep has lost her sheep,
and her father's having a fit.
But he should have known
not to leave her alone —
she's a careless little twit!

Little Bo Peep has lost her sheep —
that's the hundred and tenth time this year.
(*Now it's your turn. Make up your own lines!*)

But she didn't want to hear.

Bad Behaviour

'Danny Connolly, please pay attention.
Jean Smith, stop playing the fool.
Ivy Green, wipe that grin off your face
or see me after school.
Peter, Paul, and Elsie too,
stop that whining and bleating....
And now, if you're all ready,
we'll start this teachers' meeting.'

Spot On!

Mum said:
'Sisters should share everything —
their clothes, their toys, their socks.'
So, feeling rather generous,
I shared my chickenpox.

39

Rover

I wanted a dog,
but Dad gave me a spider
and told me his name was Rover.
He wasn't much good,
'cause, try as I would,
I couldn't get him to roll over,
and he wouldn't do 'fetch',
and he wouldn't do 'sit',
and he wouldn't even do 'beg'.
But he got one trick right:
he'd make kids scream in fright,
by crawling right up their legs.

A Waste of Space

I am a poem
to take up space.
I guess I could sit
just about any place.
I could sit up the front,
where you'd see me first,
or at the back
'cause I'm one of the worst.
If I sat in the centre
you'd skip right past,
and not even notice,
'cause you're reading so fast.
And I wouldn't mind —
not at all, not one bit —
'cause I'm taking up space.
That's my job, isn't it?

If I Ruled the World

If I ruled the world, I'd outlaw broccoli,
and have chocolate for every meal.
I'd turn my back garden into a fairground
and live in the Ferris wheel.
I'd ban all the children from going to school,
and make them watch TV instead,
and the teachers would do all our chores for us —
the nastiest ones for the Head.

Course, if I ruled the world I'd have to take charge,
and solve people's problems and stuff;
I'd have to decide how to stop all the wars,
and sort out global warming — sounds tough.
And if things went wrong, then they'd all blame me,
and I'd feel really upset and sad....
So if I ruled the world, someone else could take
            charge,
And I'd stay home with my mum and dad.

Mirror, Mirror

When I look in the mirror
I think I see me,
but some things just aren't
where they ought to be.
I've got a freckle
on my left cheek,
but in the mirror I see
it's on the right — the sneak!

Jack Sprat

Jack Sprat would eat no fats,
his wife would eat no leans,
so they've gone vegetarian
and live on soya beans.

Our Dog 3

Our dog is a golfer —
you can ask my mum.
Dad left his golf shirts out last night,
and our dog got a hole in one.

See You Later, Alligator

If you meet an alligator
getting off the bus,
just smile and say, 'I'll see you later,'
then walk away, quick, rush.

'Cause alligators have sharp teeth
and a real big appetite
and love to eat small boys and girls,
eight or nine a night.

But if by chance you can't buzz off
'cause you're too tired to run,
act real cool — take him to school,
sit back and watch the fun.

'Cause gators just love teachers,
boiled or grilled or soft,
and if he eats all your teachers
you can have the whole week off.

47

Tommy's Teacher-Eater

'Excuse me, Teacher — please, Teacher,
listen to me.' 'Yes?'
'Tommy's got a monster,
hiding in his desk.'

    'Oh, has he now? Really?
    Mm-hm, I see.'
    'Please, Teacher — listen, Teacher,
    you must believe me.

'Teacher, it looks really yukky,
all covered in slimy goo....
I want to check if it's still there,
but I can't look — will you?'

    'All right, Sam, I'll take a look,
    But just so that you'll see....
    Good gosh! There is a monster,
    And it's coming after me.'

'Run, Teacher! Go, Teacher!
It's catching up on you....
Oh, look, it's eaten Mrs Hayes!
Wow, that makes twenty-two!'

Parrot Tricks

When we pull our parrot's right leg,
he says, 'Hi-dee-hi.'
And when we pull his left leg,
he says, 'Byesie-bye.'
But if we pull both legs at once,
he doesn't even squeak;
he just tumbles off his perch
and lands
    BANG!
        right on his beak.

Grandad's New Hairstyle

Grandad's changed his hairstyle.
He changed it late last night.
He pushed one hair to the left
and the other to the right.

What Do Teenagers Have that Other Kids Do Not?

There's one thing that teenagers have that other kids do not:

it's

lots

and

lots

and

lots

and

lots

and

lots

of teenage spots.

Early Bird Special

The early bird gets the worm,
so I've heard it said,
but if the early bird were smart
he'd just eat out instead.

Mary Mary's Quite Contrary

Mary Mary's gone quite contrary
and given up growing flowers.
She's become an organic farmer,
and now she's spending hours
up to her knees in cow-dung
or painting her hen-house pink,
or mucking out her pigpens....
Boy, she don't half stink!

Wally the Wascally Weptile

Wally was a weptile,
a weally wotten one;
he'd wun awound the swamp at night
doing howwid things fo fun.

He'd wush between the wushes
chasing swamp-wats wound and wound,
until the wats got tiad
and collapsed upon the gwound.

Then he'd wam the wabbits
from the meadows to the wivah,
and woll awound with laughtah,
as the wabbits shook and shivahed.

Yes, Wally was a weptile,
a weally wotten one,
until one day when he at last
was gwounded by his mum.

(contd.)

His mum said, 'Wally, weally,
I just can't believe it's twue.
My fwiends awound the swamp wepoht
such howwid things of you.'

She said, 'My son, I'll gwound you.
Stay inside fowevah!
Wascally weptiles such as you
awe weally not that clevah.'

She told him, No' mo wunning,
no mo' wushing at the wats
o' wamming wabbits into wivahs,
'cause they weally don't like that.'

Now Wally's still a weptile,
and he's still a wotten one,
But he's sowwy 'bout wushing and wamming,
'cause now he can't have *any* fun.

Excuse Me?

My teacher is confusing me;
I wish she'd make up her mind.
Last week eighteen was six times three —
Today it's two times nine.

The Armadillo

If you should find an armadillo
sleeping soundly on your pillow,
please do not disturb the chap,
as armadillos need their nap.

And if you meet him in the hall,
Be sure to greet him, 'Hi there, y'all!'
'Cause chances are he's native Texan,
and finds other accents quite perplexin'.

Reverend Twit's Glass Bubble Church

A vicar by the name of Twit,
a man of six feet and a bit,
looked at his church and shook his head.
'This place will have to go,' he said.
'The doors hang off. The brickwork's cracked.
The whole thing's slanting front to back.
There's slimy green stuff on the ceiling.
The paint on all the walls is peeling.
In every board, in every pew,
there's a woodworm, maybe two.
The roof has holes so large they'd fit
ten elephants,' sighed Reverend Twit.

Now, being a resourceful man,
the vicar hit upon a plan
to build a church for a million pounds.
So he begged from all around,
ran Bingo every Tuesday night,
took bets on all the games and fights,
held Winter, Spring and Summer Balls
and church fairs with unusual stalls.

And when he had the money got
(believe you me, it was a lot)
he got the plans drawn up for free
by a nephew who stood six foot three.
Then he got the building done
by his sister's six-foot-seven son,
the well-known sculptor Frank Twit-Hubble,
who built a church like a great glass bubble.

Now, on that church's opening day,
when the locals came to pray,
just imagine their surprise —
they couldn't even get inside!
Not one local got a seat,
'cause the Council, the Chief of Police,
the P.M. and the House of Lords,
dignitaries from abroad,
assorted nobs and snobs and that
sat where the locals should have sat.

And as the locals stood outside
the summer sun began to shine.
And, without a hint of breeze,
the temperature jumped by degrees.

You may have heard in science class
that, when the sun's rays shine through glass,
they will create so great a heat,
it burns up wood or leaves or meat.

And so....

Soon those inside — young, old and older —
began to singe and then to smoulder,
and by the second Hallelujah
they all were smelling most peculiar.
And as they reached to hold their noses,
smoke started rising from their toeses.

Then, suddenly —
        WHOOSH —
                flames and flashes —
And the nobs and snobs were burnt to ashes.

Now on the site of that event
there stands a telling testament:
a simple plaque which says that it's
'In Memory of Three Big Twits.'

Billy the Bunny R.I.P.

Billy our bunny died last week,
and I miss him a bunch,
'cause every day since Billy died
we've had carrots for our lunch
and dinner
and tea
and supper
and breakfast....

MENU

Carrot soup
Carrot salad
Mixed carrots

Carrot surprise
Carrot stew
Carrot Quiche

"CARROT" cake
Carrot Ice cream
Carrot juice

Dog Warning

Our toothless guard dog's on patrol,
but please don't chance your luck,
'cause if he grabs you with his gums
you'll get a nasty suck.

Crossword Poem

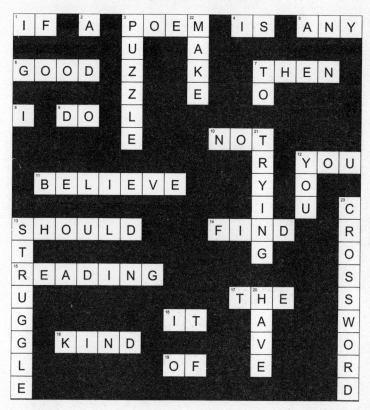

Across
1, 2, 3, 4, 5, 6, 7, 8, 9, 10, 11, 12, 13, 14, 15, 16, 17, 18, 19
Down
13, 12, 20, 21, 7, 22, 2, 23, 3

Little Miss Muffet Trilogy

Little Miss Muffet sat on her tuffet,
eating Jack Horner's home cooking.
She'd nicked it that day,
while he was at play,
and his father and mother weren't looking.

Little Miss Muffet has lost Bo Peep's sheep,
which is not one of life's great surprises.
She's no shepherd, you see,
and if you ask me,
she's got an identity crisis.

Little Miss Muffet sat on her tuffet,
Eating spaghetti. How strange!
I know that you'll say
it should have been whey —
don't *you* ever feel like a change?

Note from Tinkerbell

Give Michael back his teddy bear!
Stop stealing poor John's cup!
Wendy says you pull her hair —
Oh, Peter Pan, grow up!

Belly Buttons

'Why do we have belly buttons?'
asked my sister Flo.
'I'll tell you,' said my grandad,
'just so you will know.
You see, when God makes babies,
he stands them all in lines
and walks along inspecting them
six or seven times.
And when he's sure they're all just right,
he breaks into a run
and pokes each one in the tummy,
saying, 'You're done, you're done, you're done.'

It's All Relative

When I was very, very small,
my grandfather was very tall.
It's funny: now I'm getting taller,
Grandad's getting much, much smaller.

Jungle Fever

It's terrible, awful,
the talk of the town —
the king of the jungle
is feeling run-down.

His nose is all red
and it runs when he talks,
and his legs go all wobbly
each time that he walks.

His temperature's rocketed —
one twenty-two —
but he still feels all shivery....
What can we do?

His eyes are bright red,
his throat hurts when he speaks —
not that you can hear him:
his voice is too weak.

The lion is lying
asleep on the ground.
Shh, everyone — quiet —
don't make a sound.

'How's Your Majesty feeling?
I hope you're all right —
AAAAAAAAAGGGGH!'

Oh dear....

At least one thing's doing fine:
his appetite.

Baa Baa Bald Sheep

'Baa, baa, bald sheep, have you any wool?'
'No, sir, no, sir, not a thimbleful.
You get wool from a sheep
or a goat, that's a fact —
but me, I'm a pig,
you blind old bat!'

77

The Thing I Like about School

There's lots I like about school,
drawing and playing and things,
but the thing I like best about school
is when the school bell rings.

Bad Idea

I tickle my baby brother,
I tickle him just for fun,
I tickle him on the nose,
I tickle him on the tum,
I tickle him on the chin,
I tickle him on the feet ...
but

OUCH!

I shouldn't try to tickle him on the teeth.

A Natural Garden

Our garden's a bit of a jungle;
you never know what you'll find there —
lost girls and boys, my sister's old toys,
a table, a sofa, a chair.
So I said, 'Why can't we have roses
and flowers like everyone else?'
But Dad just said, 'Son, I think this way's more fun.
You know I designed it myself.
I mean, roses —' said Dad, 'who would want them?
Tulips? A real waste of space!
Daffs and chrysanths? They're for old maiden aunts.
Lilies? Nah, they're not my taste.
And who'd want sweet william or violets,
lavender, crocus, sweet peas,
when instead they could ramble through tall
grass and bramble
and weeds that come up to your knees?
Yes, weeds and tall grass,' Dad said proudly,
'that's a natural garden, you see.
Wind, hail or snow, it continues to grow,
and it never needs no help from me.

So make us a sandwich and put the footy on,
there's a good chap.'

The Aardvark

The reason that people don't
have aardvarks as pets, I suppose,
Is 'cause aardvarks have one nasty habit —
they shove live ants up their nose.

(Well, they don't really, but it looks like they do.)

The Collector

A collector came around last night —
a very nice young man
collecting for the old folks' home —
and so I gave him Gran.

      I hope a guy knocks on our door
      so I can say, 'Hey, Mister,
      collecting for the children's home?
      I'll give you my big sister.'

Waterfall

When we were up in Donegal
we saw a great huge waterfall,
and Róisín asked, in pure delight,
'Do they turn it off at night?'

Or Maybe a Hamster

Mum's having a baby next week —
Dad's put all the baby stuff up.
They asked me if I want a boy or a girl,
but I'd rather have a new pup.

Skool Note

Davey wuz not in skool toda
coz he ad a pane in his tum,
an he wunt be in for the resta the wek
yours sinec   sinser   cinser
Lotsa luv
My Mum

Hey Diddle ... What?

Hey diddle diddle,
the cat dumped his fiddle,
and took up the saxophone.
The cow jumped the moon,
to visit his friends,
but there was nobody home.
The little dog laughed
to see such fun,
but he howled when a fork
got stuck up his bum.
And as for Sir Dish,
and dear Miss Spoon,
she jilted him at the altar and ran away with a
totally gorgeous stew-pot instead.

Self-Defence

Gran's put on a fencing mask,
her thickest gardening gloves,
skateboarder arm- and elbow-pads,
and on her chest, the dear old love's
wrapped one of those white padded things
that baseball umpires wear,
and her legs are wrapped in cricket pads —
she's a sight, I do declare.
On top she's wearing waterproofs,
trousers, coat and hat.
'Right, now,' she says, 'I'm ready
to try and bath the cat.'

Our Dog 4

Our dog is great at DIY.
Last night Dad gave a roar —
'You stupid dog, you've ruined my shirt!' —
and our dog made a bolt for the door.

Faster than a Speeding Bullet

'Look!'
'Where?'
'Up in the sky.'
'I need the binoculars —
give me a try.'

'Oh yeah!
It's a bird ...
or maybe a plane....
Nah, it's dust on the lens.
Oh, what a pain.'

*(Actually, at that very moment, the entire superhero
population of our planet flew by on a once-off,
never-to-be-repeated family outing. But they were
so busy wiping the binoculars they didn't notice.*

Oh, well!)

The Assembled Cast

This is a drawing of Aislinn O's face —
we've put it in here
'cause this is the right place.

And this is a drawing of Aislinn O's dad —
he writes poems too
and they're not all that bad.

And this is a drawing of the illustrator —
her name is Aileen,
she's dead good (don't you hate her?)

And this is our Seamus who publishes books —
no, don't laugh, that's cruel,
this is how he looks.

And now that you've seen the assembled cast,
I bet you can guess why we put this in last.

WARNING: *Please don't show this poem to your*
little brothers or sisters. The drawings will scare
them to death.

Also from Wolfhound Press

Skyscraper Ted
And Other Zany Verse
Margot Bosonnet

Skyscraper Ted was too long for his bed,
Which posed insurmountable problems:
Should he sleep with his legs hanging over the edge,
Or his head sticking up like a goblin's?

Quirky, zany poems for kids, with wonderful wacky illustrations by Aileen Caffrey. Meet Skyscraper Ted and a host of characters from the witty pen of Margot Bosonnet.

'... one of the best Irish collections of
children's verse I've seen in a long time.'
Evening Press

ISBN 0-86327-406-4

Also from Wolfhound Press

Rusty Nails
& Astronauts

Edited by
Robert Dunbar
& Gabriel Fitzmaurice

For this wonderful anthology Robert Dunbar and Gabriel Fitzmaurice have chosen old favourites and new, poems from far and near, short poems, long poems, funny poems, sad poems, traditional and quirky, silly and serious.

Spanning 700 years and with almost 200 poems, beautifully illustrated by Marie-Louise Fitzpatrick, *Rusty Nails & Astronauts* is a book children and adults will fall in love with and treasure.

Hardback

ISBN 0-86327-671-7

Wolfhound Press
68 Mountjoy Square
Dublin 1